We Wish You A Merry Christmas

A Canadian Carol

Helaine Becker

illustrated by
Werner Zimmermann

North Winds Press
An Imprint of Scholastic Canada Ltd.

The illustrations were created with Photoshop, Procreate and
the ever-valuable backup of pencils and paper.

MENU

APPETIZERS

Library and Archives Canada Cataloguing in Publication

Title: We wish you a merry Christmas : a
Canadian carol / Helaine Becker ; illustrated
by Werner Zimmermann
Names: Becker, Helaine, author. |
Zimmermann, H. Werner, illustrator.

Identifiers: Canadiana 20210244445 | ISBN
9781443175883 (hardcover)

Subjects: LCSH: Christmas poetry. | LCSH:
Canada—Juvenile poetry.

Classification: LCC PS8553.E295532 W4
2021 | DDC jC811/.6—dc23

www.scholastic.ca

ENTREES

Text copyright © 2021 by Helaine Becker.

Illustrations copyright © 2021 by Werner
Zimmermann.

5 4 3 2   Printed in China 38   22 23 24 25

For Canada's kids.
I love you!
— H.B.

To Lori with love.
— W.Z.

Good tidings to you, and all of your kin,
We wish you a Merry Christmas and a Happy New Year!

Now bring us some figgy pudding,
Now bring us some figgy pudding,
Now bring us some figgy pudding,
Please bring some right here!

We won't go until we get some,
We won't go until we get some,
We won't go until we get some,
So bring some out here!

We wish you a Merry Christmas,
We wish you a Merry Christmas,
We wish you a Merry Christmas
and a Happy New Year!

9

Now bring us some twigs to chew on,
Now bring us some twigs to chew on,
Now bring us some twigs to chew on,
Please bring some right here!

We won't go until we get some,
We won't go until we get some,
We won't go until we get some,
Just bring some right here!

Now bring us some juicy herring,
Now bring us some juicy herring,
Now bring us some juicy herring,
Just slap some down here!

14

We won't go until we get some,
We won't go until we get some,
We won't go until we get some,
So slap 'em down here!

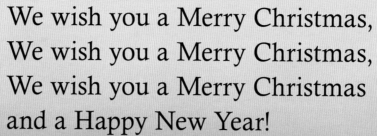

We wish you a Merry Christmas,
We wish you a Merry Christmas,
We wish you a Merry Christmas
and a Happy New Year!

16

And bring us some crunchy acorns,
And bring us some crunchy acorns,
And bring us some crunchy acorns,
Please bring some right here!

We won't go until we get some,
We won't go until we get some,
We won't go until we get some,
So bring some right here!

Now bring us some tasty berries,
Now bring us some tasty berries,
Now bring us some tasty berries,
Please bring some right here!

20

We won't go until we get some,
We won't go until we get some,
We won't go until we get some,
Just bring some right here!

Now bring us some stinky pudding,
Now bring us some stinky pudding,
Now bring us some stinky pudding,
Please bring some right here!

We won't go until we get some,
We won't go until we get some,
We won't go until we get some,
We smell some in here!

23

We wish you a Merry Christmas,
We wish you a Merry Christmas,
We wish you a Merry Christmas
and a Happy New Year!

Now bring us some maple doughnuts,
Now bring us some maple doughnuts,
Now bring us some maple doughnuts,
Please bring some right here!

We won't go until we get some,
We won't go until we get some,
We won't go until we get some,
So bring some right here!

Good tidings to you, and all of your kin,
We wish you a Merry Christmas and a Happy New Year!